THIS IS ME! 2022

CREATIVE WONDERS

Edited By Andy Porter

First published in Great Britain in 2022 by:

Young Writers
Remus House
Coltsfoot Drive
Peterborough
PE2 9BF
Telephone: 01733 890066
Website: www.youngwriters.co.uk

Book Design by Ashley Janson

Softback ISBN 978-1-80459-071-3

Printed and bound in the UK by BookPrintingUK
Website: www.bookprintinguk.com
YB0510U

FOREWORD

For Young Writers' latest competition This Is Me, we asked primary school pupils to look inside themselves, to think about what makes them unique, and then write a poem about it! They rose to the challenge magnificently and the result is this fantastic collection of poems in a variety of poetic styles.

Here at Young Writers our aim is to encourage creativity in children and to inspire a love of the written word, so it's great to get such an amazing response, with some absolutely fantastic poems. It's important for children to focus on and celebrate themselves and this competition allowed them to write freely and honestly, celebrating what makes them great, expressing their hopes and fears, or simply writing about their favourite things. This Is Me gave them the power of words. The result is a collection of inspirational and moving poems that also showcase their creativity and writing ability.

I'd like to congratulate all the young poets in this anthology, I hope this inspires them to continue with their creative writing.

CONTENTS

THE POEMS

Magic Artist

I'm going to tell you about myself with a little rhyme...
My name is Ivie and I am nine
My hair is long and the colour of the sunset and my eyes are like the ocean
I am kind and funny and my mum says that I am full of emotions
But I am also a big sis, which is probably why...
I am only joking, she's the apple of my eye.
My dog's called Max and he's a chocolate Labrador.
He is my first fluffy friend, but I am trying to get my dad to get a new one.
When I am older I want art to be my career
And I want enough money to visit New York every year.
Harry Potter is my biggest obsession
And if I don't make it as an artist I will happily work as a witch at Hogwarts as my profession.
Hope you enjoyed my poem,
Lots of love,
Ivie.

Ivie Brown (9)
Blakehill Primary School, Idle

This Is Me

My name is Harper and I like my pencil to be sharper.
I like cats and dogs, just not frogs.
I like to catch my pets in big, old nets.
I like to cook and read a good book.
I have a dog that loves to bark but not in the dark.
I love to pick a flower every hour at the park.
It's the end of the poem, I'm sorry to say but I hope you all have a very good day.

Harper Grace Carter-Worrall (8)
Bradway Primary School, Bradway

This Is Me

My eyes are as blue as the sky.
My hair is as brown as chocolate.
My lips are as thin as a pencil.
My hands are as small as an ant.
My teeth are as strong as an elephant.

Phoebe Pigg
Bradway Primary School, Bradway

When I Play Rugby

When I play rugby...
I step onto the pitch,
I feel like I can do anything,
It gives courage,
I am flying and free.

When I play rugby...
I forget everything,
The ball comes running towards me,
I am like a giant,
The ball is gold to me,
I thunder across holding the treasure,
I place it on the try-line,
I feel like I am a precious jewel.

When I play rugby...
I am stronger than ever,
I feel like the queen,
The world around me disappears,
Just my team and I on the pitch,
Nobody can touch me,

The sun comes out even on the rainiest days,
When I am on the pitch of mud and grass,
I am unstoppable.

Ruby Winzer (9)

East Allington Primary School, East Allington

Japan Is Me

When I see Japan
I am contented,
Those bright lights
Are my true love.
My eyes are full of wonder,
I would do anything to be there.

The blossom makes my mind clear,
All those things are beaten
The smell of the pink petaled tree fills my nose,
The slight breeze brushes my skin,
The water gently ripples,
My grey clouds disappear,
I am left with blossom,
Swinging back and forth,
It's like they're saying hello.

When I go to Japan,
I will be free -
All the photos I see will be a dream now,
But soon will not

A tear runs down my cheek,
I will be me.

Isabella Centore (10)
East Allington Primary School, East Allington

Horse Riding

When I ride a horse,
I feel like all my troubles disappear into the blue
The tack as I gallop across the open green field
Jingles in the sunset
When I ride my horse,
I feel like I'm flying above the clouds,
I sit back and let the wind blow in my hair
When I ride my horse I feel like I can do anything
As I jump over the poles
There is a good feeling that travels up through my bones into my heart
When I ride my horse
It feels like the horse understands me
It was like it was there when my troubles were building up
As soon as I get on my horse it suddenly resolves my problems.

Halle Trout-Cooper (11)
East Allington Primary School, East Allington

Skateboarding

When I go on my skateboard,
I can be who I want to be, the world freezes, the anger and drama of my life drifts - away.

When I go on my skateboard,
I can just let go of everything and the bumps from under my feet reassure me, every single thing is going to be okay.

When I go on my skateboard,
The wind blows in my hair - I breathe in a calm gulp of fresh air and blow it out even calmer.

It feels like I'm immortal like there's no ending of this wonderful world.
I roll and roll
Without control
With no worry in the world.

Nell Jones (9)
East Allington Primary School, East Allington

When I Am Farming

When I am farming I am unstoppable,
I can do anything and I don't have a care in the world.

When I am farming I am like a wild bull,
When charging through the green fields on my Ford.

When I am farming I can drive my tractor anywhere,
Under the sparkling black sky.

When I am farming I drive my old rusted Ford,
Through the fields of golden grain,
With my sheepdog Patch.

When I am farming I look after baby animals.
I will bottle feed them on my lap,
Or I will warm them in front of the fire.

Harry Higgin (10)
East Allington Primary School, East Allington

Farmer Lads

When I drive a tractor
I feel free
Like I am flying; my troubles melt away

When I drive a tractor
I sit next to the king
I hear the tractor humming
My childhood songs

When I drive a tractor
Birds sing
And the glow of evening light comes out

When I drive my tractor
Sun comes out to warm the golden grain
The wheat feels soft and warm in my hands;

When I drive a tractor
It smells of dark smoke
When I drive a tractor I am giving people food.

Charlie Horswill (10)
East Allington Primary School, East Allington

Boxing Rules

When I do boxing I feel like there's nothing to stop me,
I punch through the brick walls to victory,
When I do boxing I am a champion,
I batter the bag till my heart is pounding like someone who's just run a marathon.

When I do boxing I work and work for the belt,
I feel the sweat dripping from my face,
When I do boxing all my thoughts go away about school,
I let my arm swing as hard as I can,
I am super fast and try to beat everyone else,
When I do boxing I feel tremendous.

Henry Pittman (9)
East Allington Primary School, East Allington

When I Play Football I'm A King

When I play football I'm a king,
Cheers from the crowd echo all around the stadium
Cheering my name, "Finley! Finley!"

When I play football I'm a king,
Letting nobody past me like a brick wall,
When I play I feel like I'm a champion of the world!

When I play football I'm a king,
I'm like a tiger ready to pounce on my prey,
The crowd goes quiet,
The penalty is mine to take,
I score!
Roars from the crowd deafen my ears.

Finley Gogola (11)
East Allington Primary School, East Allington

Golden Goalie

When I play in goal,
I feel unstoppable,
Like I can reach the sky with ease,
When I play in goal,
I feel like an impenetrable fortress that the attackers cannot hope to get anywhere near,
When I play in goal I inhale the scent of victory and it makes me work harder and faster,
When I play in goal,
I feel like nothing can go wrong,
Like all my worries melt away,
And at the end of the day,
I feel like I have done something incredible.

Aldous Noott Browning (11)
East Allington Primary School, East Allington

When I Sing

When I sing,
It feels like all my worries melt away,
I can feel the warm sun touch my skin as it comes out
Shining a spotlight on me.

When I sing,
It feels like the world stops for a minute
Just to hear me,
I can feel my happiness break through the darkness.

When I sing,
It feels like I can fly far and free and touch the clouds,
I close my eyes, I can see everything I love,
I know I am okay.

Isabella Brooker (9)
East Allington Primary School, East Allington

When I Ride My Horse

When I ride my horse,
I zone out from the rest of the world,
Just me and my horse
In a beautiful meadow of dandelion and wildflowers.

When I ride my horse,
I forget the worries of school,
I'm buzzing with happiness,
Not like a crumpled piece of paper on the floor.

When I ride my horse,
I hear the bees buzz,
And the smell of honey rushes into my face
As we ride into the golden sunset.

Chloe Gilbert (10)
East Allington Primary School, East Allington

When I Ride My Horse

When I ride my horse
I feel like I am flying with the birds when jumping the pole
And my troubles drift away in the wind
When I ride my horse
I feel like a queen
Riding in a bright warm field
When I ride my horse
My body sinks into the saddle
And the horse's mane tickles my hand as it moves side to side
When I ride my horse
I get to be myself
To feel free
I can do anything I want to do.

Phoebe Tucker (9)
East Allington Primary School, East Allington

When I Play Rugby

When I play rugby
I feel free like I can do anything
It's like I'm a bird that's been freed from its cage

When I play rugby
I can feel the winter breeze on my face
While I'm running up and down the ginormous field

When I play rugby
I'm faster than a cheetah and more sly than a cat
I race across the field faster than a lion chasing its prey.

Elsie Tucker (9)
East Allington Primary School, East Allington

Farm Boys Rule

When I drive my quad,
I feel the cold air on
My ears - the squelching mud
As I'm drifting around corners.

When I drive my quad,
All my thoughts about school go away,
It is all about
The farm and the cows.

When I drive my quad,
It is so joyful,
Listening to the cows, sheep,
Pigs and chickens,
It is the best experience I've ever had.

Kaiden Coleman-Sanders (10)
East Allington Primary School, East Allington

When I Play Football

When I play football,
I feel free,
I feel like a rhino charging at the goal.

When I play football,
I kick the ball and listen to it whistle,
And it will always go into the back of the net.

When I play football,
I will never miss a shot,
I'm always on target.

When I play football,
I'm the colour of the pitch, I'm the firework.

George Mitchell (10)
East Allington Primary School, East Allington

Farmer Lads

When I drive my tractor,
I feel cool as the wind blows through the window.
I hear the tractor humming my song.

When I drive my tractor, I feel free as I bounce up and down on the seat,
Thick slabs of crumbling earth underneath.
When I step out of my tractor the golden air is warm on my skin.

I am happy when I drive my tractor.

Toby Newnham (10)
East Allington Primary School, East Allington

My Quad And Me

When I drive my quad I feel free,
I am the king,
Like I'm gliding through the air.

When I drive my quad I'm undefeatable,
Unstoppable,
I am a rhino charging around,
Running free.

When I drive my quad I am in a different world,
I am driving for miles on end,
My metallic friend helps me all the way.

Albert Barons (9)
East Allington Primary School, East Allington

The Farmer Boy

When I drive my tractor
I feel calm
My metallic friend is in the field breaking up the ground
Being on the farm is really fun
And when I am helping Dad on the farm
When I drive a tractor
In the field I crumble the ground
When I drive my tractor
The warm wheat weighs heavily
Like gold in my hands.

Jacob Lethbridge
East Allington Primary School, East Allington

Get To Know All About Me

Hello, I am Shakira, I am eleven years old.
I have two pets, one cat called Bebo and one dog, Hugo.
I love them both and I have an older sister.
I am a year six pupil.
I like to express myself through drawing and dance.
When I am upset or angry I like to draw or dance.
I feel like dance and drawing are a part of me.
I love doing new things.
If I can help, I will.
I love helping other people because it is kind.

Shakira Harakuta (11)
English Martyrs Catholic Primary School, Wakefield

This Is Ciara

T ea, I love tea
H elpful and happy, that's me
I ncredibly smart
S uper silly but sensible

I love my family
S andwiches are my favourite

C aring, crazy, that is me
I love dancing, it's my favourite thing
A va's my sister and so that be
R ainbows are colourful just like me
A re you ready to see me?

Ciara Tarrush (10)
English Martyrs Catholic Primary School, Wakefield

Layla Coates

This is me and I am not ashamed

L oving
A mazing dancer
Y our favourite
L ove my family
A bsolute superstar

C aring and creative
O bservant
A ppreciative
T alented
E nthusiastic
S uperstar

This is me
I have no apologies.

Layla Coates (11)
English Martyrs Catholic Primary School, Wakefield

This Is Me

T his is me, I don't care what other people think
H ate slapping
I have two brothers and a sister
S chool is the best ever

I like pizza
S tubborn, that is what my mum and dad said

M any talents like gymnastics and football
E nergetic person.

Amy Belk (10)
English Martyrs Catholic Primary School, Wakefield

Skating

S kating is me, rolling and free
K eep on going, your troubles roll away
A dore myself when I'm skating free
T ackling new skills, shining so bright
I nspire myself to always do best
N ever give up, try, try, try
G rowing in skills and learning to be me.

Liliana Omono (11)
English Martyrs Catholic Primary School, Wakefield

Football!

Football is my passion
Football is the best
Football is my favourite
Football is nice
Football is my passion
And that's the end of my fantastic poem.

Noah Speight (11)
English Martyrs Catholic Primary School, Wakefield

My Thing

I draw what I see, I add something from my imagination
R eading, I do my thing, although I don't do it all the time
I think about what to draw, read, photograph
S ome say I'm weird but I think I'm just as weird as everyone else.

Iris Ann Philips (9)
Glassary Primary School, Lochgilphead

The Poem That Will Bring You Four Things You Need

This poem will bring you happiness, love,
friendliness and care.
This is me.

C ool for being a good friend
A chieving making people proud
R ights for being a child
E specially kind.

I hope you enjoyed.

Keira Chamberlain (9)
Glassary Primary School, Lochgilphead

The Eilidh Acrostic

E asily distracted by sloths
I am energetic like a lion
L ove cars
I love shinty and all sports
D oing silly things
H appy all the time with my friends.

Eilidh Cameron (10)
Glassary Primary School, Lochgilphead

Frazer

F ootball is life
R unning after sheep
A sheep farmer
Z oos are my favourite
E nergetic
R angers fan.

Frazer Prentice (10)

Glassary Primary School, Lochgilphead

Horse Land

H orse riding
O ver the jumps
R iding along the fields
S unset disappears
E at the tasty dinner.

Aimee Mactavish (11)
Glassary Primary School, Lochgilphead

This Is Kali

K ittens, cats, dogs, I love them all!
A good gamer
L oud and energetic
I 'm weird but I'm nice!

Kali McCuaig (11)
Glassary Primary School, Lochgilphead

Lots Of Kgs

20300g of adventure
50kg of happiness
200g of love
10,000g of loudness
Mix it then put it in the oven.

Lena Henderson (8)
Glassary Primary School, Lochgilphead

All About Ewan

E pic at video games
W atches many movies
A football player
N ever give up.

Ewan Mitchell (11)
Glassary Primary School, Lochgilphead

Abby

A wesome at
B aking
B eautiful inside and out
Y oung child.

Abby Simpson (11)
Glassary Primary School, Lochgilphead

When I Went To The Beach!

On Monday I went to the beach and saw one
wonderful octopus, giggling all the time.
On Tuesday I went to the beach and saw two
terrific turtles, swimming all the time.
On Wednesday I went to the beach and saw three
cheeky crabs, stealing sandwiches all the time.
On Thursday I went to the beach and saw four
funny fish, feeling jocular all the time.
On Friday I went to the beach and saw five stoked
starfish, satisfied all the time.
On Saturday I went to the beach and saw six
sparkling seagulls, making noise all the time.
On Sunday I went to the beach and saw seven
dancing dolphins, diving all the time.
When I went to the beach, I felt the magic begin...

Pavinaa Rakulan (11)
Grange Park Junior School, Hayes

What Makes Me?

What makes me?
Let us see!
The first ingredient to make me
Is a splash of chattiness,
And a sprinkle of determination!
Our second ingredient is...
A jug of kindness
A pinch of drama
Our last ingredient is...
A handful of smiles
And a barrel of smartness!
Slide it into the oven
And watch it burst with happiness
As it comes out
As you slice it open
You find yourself jumping energetically

When you cut another slice
It is full of fun and creativity!

Are you like me?

Riya Saini (11)
Grange Park Junior School, Hayes

Love Is All Around The World

All around the Earth is love, love, love
All these good behaviours are above, above, above
What I like to show is care and I share
My dream is to become a doctor and to help others
Being kind is me and I like my family
When I am alone I get really worried
But when my friends are there I'm ready, ready, ready
I love the world and I am happy that it is made
All around the world, everyone has love.

Venus W-W J (8)
Grange Park Junior School, Hayes

Chocolate

C hocolate is my favourite snack
H appiness is the best feeling in the world
O pen-hearted human being
C elebrating birthdays is fun
O range is my favourite colour
L ego is a very exciting toy to play with
A lways like to play video games
T esla is my favourite car
E lectric vehicles are environmentally friendly.

Monish Rajan (8)
Grange Park Junior School, Hayes

The Cat And The Rat

There once was a cat who had a hat
And he went flat because of the bat.
Then he saw a dog and the cat
Went flying over the rat
Into the window.
The rat went running to the cat
And the cat hurt its back.
So the rat helped the cat
Then the cat slapped the rat.
In the end, the cat and the rat
Became friends and travelled the world together.

Alina C (8)

Grange Park Junior School, Hayes

What I Like

I like to draw
I like to paint
I like to play
I like to sketch
I like to colour
I like to do my homework
My favourite subject is art
My favourite sport is football
My favourite food is noodles
My favourite day is Friday
My favourite number is 100
My favourite fruit is strawberry.

Vaneet Kaur (7)
Grange Park Junior School, Hayes

Personality

I'm shining like a star,
But on Planet Earth,
I'm proud to be,
As this is me,

The joy of life,
Surrounding myself,
Respect and bravery,
Comes in mystery,

My past life,
Is working so hard,
Step by step,
From one to ten...

Oviya Sureshkumar (10)
Grange Park Junior School, Hayes

Yasmin In Colours

My favourite colour is pink
It's beautiful, don't you think?
The mud is brown,
More like a town.
Blood is red, also like heads!
My eyes are blue,
I am writing, which is due,
My dressing table is purple,
Don't you think it's like a turtle?

Yasmin Jaleel (7)
Grange Park Junior School, Hayes

This Is Me

T his is me
H aving fun
I get to bake with my family
S ometimes I go to get a lolly

I love my favourite toy
S o I sleep with it

M angoes are what I mostly eat
E lephants get fed with mangoes.

Koshini Selvaranjan (9)
Grange Park Junior School, Hayes

This Is Me

T his is me
H aving fun while reading
I hate science and RE
S o I just do English, maths and topic

I love to play
S o I get five minutes

M e, I care for my family
E ven if they care for me!

Kasvini Kaanthan (8)
Grange Park Junior School, Hayes

Humble

H elping others in need
U nderstand others' problems
M aking me and my peers thrive
B eing the best I can be in every possible opportunity
L ikes to be polite and welcoming to others
E njoys benefitting others.

Mahathy Mutturajah (8)
Grange Park Junior School, Hayes

Birthday

B e the best you can be
I magine what you can do
R emember who you are
T here's nobody like you
H onour your past
D well on your birth
A ll you need is love
Y our birthday is a start.

Ayushmaan Saxena (8)
Grange Park Junior School, Hayes

Cool Kaya

My name is Kaya and I bring the fire
Open your eyes, the truth is I'm a busy bee
My mind flows with ideas and dreams that expand explosively in my body
When I run so passionately my curls flow so majestically
And that's a bit about me.

Kaya Lashley (11)
Grange Park Junior School, Hayes

I Am Amy

I'm as sleepy as a sloth,
As dark as a day,
You will be lucky if I stay the day.

My powers can turn on the showers,
I'm as busy as a bee,
I never stop to pee,
After the day I don't stay.

Down at the stables I stay there,
Helping May.

Maths makes me go crazy,
Then I get lazy, then I play with Maisie,
But she goes crazy so I go back to being lazy.

Elsa runs with her puns and eats toffee on Lottie the potty.

When I'm happy I read Dork Diaries,
Then I go crazy.

When I'm unhappy I have a hug with Mummy.

Salt and vinegar Pringles make me tingle.

Amy
Musbury Primary School, Musbury

Stupid Semicolons

Stupid semicolons
Stupid semicolons,
Don't make sense,
Just use a comma,
They make more sense,
Stupid semicolons,
Don't make sense,
They're just useless,
And you know it's *true*.

Commas are cool,
Yes, they are,
They work really well,
You know it's true,
They work in,
Lists,
They work as,
Breaths,
Yes, they do,
Commas are cool,
Do you think it's true?
Because I do.

Elfred
Musbury Primary School, Musbury

This Is Me!

Swimming strong and trying my best.
Music and football, I always make it a test.
I love to run and push myself to fight and win a race.
I am as fast as a cheetah and as smart as a mouse.
I am as happy as a giant and as jumpy as a kangaroo.
I am as calm as a crab and as sporty as a dog.
I love to play pool and darts at the bar.
I always play them when I go to the bar with my dad.
I love my dog very much because I love him and he loves me and this is me.

Kris Friel
St Columba's Primary School, Clady Umey

This Is Me!

Welding and hammering
Outside all day
Over at the shed diffing and diffing away
Work all day without a cup of tea
Only way they can take me away is an emergency
Rusty trailers will not do
Knock of a hammer, good as new
Circular saw I love to use
Always difficult when it blows a fuse
Running around, so much to do
Painting diggers, yes it's true
Engines roaring, makes me smile
Noisy machines make it worthwhile
Time, not enough hours in the day
Ready to hit the hay.

Billy Gordon (11)
St Columba's Primary School, Clady Umey

This Is Me

T his is me
H omework is my superpower
I like to draw
S inging is my favourite hobby.

I like to learn new things
S paghetti is my favourite food.

M y best friend is Saoirse
E than and Evan are my brothers.

D arius is
A mazing
R eally good
I nspirational
U nique
S inging superstar.

Darius McCormick
St Columba's Primary School, Clady Umey

This Is Me

Let me tell you about me
I love the YouTuber Adam B
I love to sing, dance and draw
I especially love when Millie gives me her paw.

It all started on Tuesday 4th October 2011
Weighing seven pounds seven ounces
Saoirse Mariah McGarrigle was born.

Fast forward a few years and straight to school
Making friends is super cool
Art, RE and topic are the best
But doing homework I detest.

Saoirse McGarrigle
St Columba's Primary School, Clady Umey

This Is Me

I'm the superstar at art.
I can even draw a heart.
My hair is black just like the dark.
My family is the one that brings the smile.
We watch and talk all the while.
My dream pet is a dog.
I beg and beg but nothing comes along.
I have hazel eyes just like a nut.
I'm a good dancer and runner.
I'm brave, don't shame, don't come here.
I'm the best at this game, don't come near.

Alona Lijo
St Columba's Primary School, Clady Umey

My Life

I am
Drowsy
Fun
Football mad
Sometimes I'm bad
I like art
Because I can leave my mark
The seaside is the best
After swimming, I rest
Reading is calm
Greek mythology, I'm a fan
Video games are insane
They're built into my brain
Right foot bang, it's over the bar
That's a point on the board
Guess what I scored
That's my life pretty much
I know it's not a bunch
See you later, I don't like alligators.

Mark Nelis (11)
St Columba's Primary School, Clady Umey

This Is Me

I am
Athletic
Smart
Maths is my art
Summer is cool
Because I can get in the pool
Tyrone is the best
Better than the rest
I am a daring defender
And I play in the centre
Series of Unfortunate Events
Count Olaf Is not a gent
The Baudelaires are wise
But Count Olaf is always in disguise
Online games are fun
Missions, tasks and always on the run.

Oisin Sweeney (10)
St Columba's Primary School, Clady Umey

Gaelic

G oing for a point, I score a goal
A fter that, I go for more
E nd of that, let's go home
L et's put our feet up now that we are home
I n the house, almost asleep, Mummy comes in
with something to eat
C risps, chocolate, sweets while I am almost
asleep.

Charlie Duffy
St Columba's Primary School, Clady Umey

This Is Me

G oing for a score
A lways something I will adore
E very day I get better and better
L oving it even though sometimes I get wetter and wetter
I nvolved with all the boys no matter the weather
C rying, laughing and joking together.

Harry Sweeney
St Columba's Primary School, Clady Umey

This Is Me!

This is me!
I am,
A football lover
Also a boxing lover,
A curious explorer,
Travelling I adore,
Spending time with my fifteen cousins,
Sometimes getting up to mischief always leads to trouble,
Playing outside at school I love,
The sweets I do not like, their name is milk duds,
This is me!

Caiden McMonagle
St Columba's Primary School, Clady Umey

This Is Me

My name is Mahra
And I have brown hair
When I walk on the beach
The wind blows my hair
I like to play games
And winning is my aim
When I lose to my brother
It gives me a lot of bother
I like to eat fish
It is my favourite dish
Although I can be drastic
I think I am fantastic.

Mahra McLaughlin
St Columba's Primary School, Clady Umey

This Is Me

Let me tell you about me,
I like,
Watching YouTube,
Eating sweets,
Playing video games,
Reading books,
Playing with my dog,
Drawing pictures,
Watching movies,
Playing board games,
Solving Rubik's cubes,
Finally, waking up on Christmas morning.

Harry McLaughlin (10)
St Columba's Primary School, Clady Umey

This Is Me

My name is Annie Duffy
I think I am funny
Swimming is my passion
I am very indecisive when it comes to fashion
I love my family and friends
Hope it never ends
I have brown hair and greyish blue eyes
And that's me!

Annie Duffy (10)
St Columba's Primary School, Clady Umey

Why My Dog Is The Best

B ubba is a bit crazy.
U sed to be kind of lazy.
B ubba is very fun.
B ubba also loves to play with everyone.
A nd that's why Bubba is the best.

Charlie Langan (10)
St Columba's Primary School, Clady Umey

This Is Me

This is me.

G ames, laughter, lots of fun
A lways hiding or on the run.
M issions and tasks
I nvading with masks.
N otorious is my motto
G rand Theft Auto.

Declan Mc Crory
St Columba's Primary School, Clady Umey

The Recipe To Make The Perfect Me

The recipe to make the perfect me:
First, find a tear of love
A drop of joy,
A tear of kindness,
A drop of chocolate.

Firstly, add the tear of love. This will provide inner beauty.
Secondly, slowly add the drop of joy. I always aim to bring joy to everyone I meet.
Then add the tear of kindness. Putting a smile on everyone's faces makes a huge difference.
Afterwards, add the drop of chocolate - who doesn't like chocolate!
Being careful not to split the mixture, stir slowly.
Finally, place the mixture in the oven for ten to fifteen minutes.
Sit back, relax and let me do the rest.

Booth (9)

St Ignatius Catholic Primary School, Ossett

A Spell To Make Me

A whole bag of love and kindness.
200 grams of awesomeness.
Fifty grams of fearlessness.
Twenty-five grams of loneliness.
One billion grams of messiness.
400 grams of sportiness.
200 grams of chilled.
200 grams of adventure.
A sprinkle of kindness.
As much happiness as you want.
A football.

Method:
Mix 200 grams of awesomeness with fifty grams of fearlessness.
In a separate dimension, add the twenty-five grams of loneliness, the messiness and the sportiness together.
Heat the two personalities together with chilled, adventure and as much happiness as you want and a football for talent.

Add a whole bag of happiness.
Once finished, add an extra bit of kindness.

Eliza Mumby (11)
St Ignatius Catholic Primary School, Ossett

This Is Me! Recipe

Loves dogs
Enjoys watching Netflix
Terrible animator
Loves ramen
Exotic imagination
Crayon
Creativeness
Amazon.

Instructions:
Add three teaspoons of loving dogs
Next, take twelve bags of watching Netflix
Sprinkle in a bucket of being a terrible animator
Fill a bath of loving ramen
Mix in seven cups of an exotic imagination
Chuck in a whole box of orange Crayola crayons (not edible)
Locate a jar of creativity
Don't forget to include bags of Amazon.

Now you have all of the ingredients, add it all to the bowl and thoroughly stir until you have a smooth, thick consistency.

Put the cake mixture into a cake tin, and relax in front of the fire as your cake rises.

Lucia C
St Ignatius Catholic Primary School, Ossett

This Is Me

B est food is Nutella on bread.
E ating is something I don't do very hastily.
T eddies stacked on my bed.
S trawberries are tasty.
Y ears go by and now I'm ten.

T otoro is my favourite thing.
H ave I mentioned my love of frogs?
I have a ton of siblings.
S weep is my cute and lovely dog.

I am a great artist.
S ometimes I think I'm the smartest.

M y only dream is to be someone's art teacher.
E very time I draw a picture, I feel there is a missing feature.

This is me!

Betsy R
St Ignatius Catholic Primary School, Ossett

This Is Me

You will need to make me:
A sprinkle of fun and laughter
A cosy, book-filled bedroom
A bottle of brightness
And a sprinkle of delicious food.

Recipe:
Before you start, get a big bowl and a giant wooden spoon.
Move to the book-filled bedroom and prepare to make me.
Firstly, add the fun and laughter and mix it up to brew.
Secondly, slowly add the brightness, not too fast, not too slow.
Next, add the small yet powerful sprinkle of delicious food and leave to simmer.
And lastly, this... is... me!

Charlie H (10)
St Ignatius Catholic Primary School, Ossett

This Is Me

T he one and only William H
H appy and cheerful every day
I ncredibly kind and caring to everyone
S ome people call me silly and loud.

I ngeniously fun and fantastic
S uper at computing and maths, not so good at arts and crafts.

M y brother is cheeky sometimes, but really, he is just too kind
E veryone in my family is kind and we stick together like a bind in a knot.

This is me!

William H
St Ignatius Catholic Primary School, Ossett

All About Me

I'm as fast as a cheetah
And as buzzed as a bee
Covered in plasters
Yes, that's me.

I'm as shy as a wolf
But as brave as a tiger
I'm as loyal as a dog
But can't keep my secrets.

I like football and much more
Even though I'm mostly very bored
And I love my family more than anything
And I'll love them even more.

Lewis Lupton (11)
St Ignatius Catholic Primary School, Ossett

What I Love

W hy I love pigs, they are so cute
H ow do I get upset when someone upsets me?
A va is my best friend
T hings I love: Ava, my friends and family.

I think that everyone should be happy.

L ove is everlasting
O li is amazing
V ery creative
E ebie is my loving, caring sister.

Olivia-Grace Goodall-Travis (11)
St Ignatius Catholic Primary School, Ossett

This Is Me!

T homas R, the one and only.
H owever, if you did not know, I can do 100 star jumps in under five minutes.
O liver is my best friend and when I'm sad he cheers me up.
M eant to keep my friends company.
A lways there for my family.
S haring is what I do to keep happiness flowing around the room.

Thomas Richardson (10)
St Ignatius Catholic Primary School, Ossett

This Is Me

I am as fast as a cheetah
I am as smart as a historian
I swim as fast as Adam Peaty
I like playing with my baby sister
When I'm at school I really miss her
She may get on my nerves but I still love her
I have fun in art but not so much with maths - yet!
Everyone has a hidden ability
The key to life is love, not hostility.

This is me, Oliver C.

Oliver C (9)
St Ignatius Catholic Primary School, Ossett

This Is Me

I love to ice skate with my dad
Reading books about dragons and knights
Lego makes me feel happy and calm.

McDonald's tastes good, my favourite food
My pet dragon Alphonse breathes fire
I enjoyed mini-golf with Nanan.

I am kind when I play games
I like riding on my scooter in the park with my friends
I laugh with my lovely mum.

Edward McGinn (10)
St Ignatius Catholic Primary School, Ossett

This Is Me

T he thing I am good at is football: I love Chelsea!
H ave fun!
I have lush hair and blue marbles in my eyes.
S ometimes I go to the games.

I love football until I die.
S ome of my family don't like football.

M y life is the best.
E ager to get better at the sport!

This is me.

Jacob S (10)
St Ignatius Catholic Primary School, Ossett

Brooklyn

B est person to talk to
R uns around like crazy every day
O nly plays with Liv, my BFF
O livia/Liv is my BFF
K atie/me is crazy
L oves movies and games
Y es, never says no
N o, I don't like the word.

Katie Hanks (11)
St Ignatius Catholic Primary School, Ossett

This Is Me! I Am...

G reat at listening and learning. I am
E nergetic when I play football. I am
O rganised with my work. I am
R eliable in most things. I am
G rateful for everything I have. I am
E ager to learn new things every day.

This is me
I am George.

George Pitchforth (10)
St Ignatius Catholic Primary School, Ossett

Pro-Gamer

P laying sports.
R eads books.
O ccasional movie watcher.
-
G ame player.
A nimals.
M ums and dads are amazing.
E njoys soft things.
R ugby player.

Noah O'Kane (10)
St Ignatius Catholic Primary School, Ossett

This Is Me

I'm creative, crazy,
Loud, imaginative,
Imaginative, funny, weird.

Very loud.

Yep, I'm the crazy one, that's me,
The one and only me!
A dash of creativity,
A sprinkle of clumsiness,
A squirt of funniness,
A splash of weirdness.

Ivy Walton (9)
St Ignatius Catholic Primary School, Ossett

This Is Me

T alking to my friends,
H aving fun,
I nconclusive,
S trong.

I love basketball,
S mart.

M y favourite player was Kobe Bryant,
E xciting.

Connor Ineson (11)

St Ignatius Catholic Primary School, Ossett

This Is Me

B e yourself
E at healthy to have a positive mindset
T alk to everyone, even if they are not your friend
H elping others
A mazing
N ice
Y ou are unique.

Bethany Smith (11)
St Ignatius Catholic Primary School, Ossett

The One And Only Lewis Cox

L ovely and kind person
E ager, enthusiastic but also enjoyable
W itty, have a great sense of humour
I like to game and play football
S eeing people happy makes me happy.

This is me!

Lewis C (10)
St Ignatius Catholic Primary School, Ossett

My Favourite Sports

S porty
H appy
A mazing on the football and rugby field
R ugby is my favourite
K indness
S trong.

Seth Walton (11)
St Ignatius Catholic Primary School, Ossett

Smarties Clubs

Marshmallows, sweets and gummies make me.
I am smart, but also I love maths.
ICT is also my favourite thing.
Art is awesome because we made beautiful, easy totem poles.
I like to eat jelly drinks, fish and chips, oranges, crumpets and McDonald's.
I even have piano lessons every Tuesday and I love playing the piano.
Finally, I love everything.
P.S. I love, love, love fractions!

Ying Jie Yu (8)
St John's CE Primary Academy, Stafford

Mums And Dads

Mums and dads I am talking about.
I don't mean the game or playing about in a waterspout.
Your dad is a very good lad and your mum hums better than a hummingbird.
You will need your parents, otherwise who would make dinner, right?
Our parents are as amazing as a rainbow.

Jeshikha Gurung (7)
St John's CE Primary Academy, Stafford

This Is Me

I like to play tennis
I like crazy golf
I like to bike ride
When the weather is nice.

I like to eat chocolate
I especially like cake
Combine them together
To make yummy chocolate cake.

I'm great at swimming
I like to run
Digging big holes in the sun
Is a lot of fun.

Holidays, trips to the park
Playing games, having a laugh
Adventurous days, whatever the weather
Loving these memories we make together.

This is me.

Ollie Weaver (9)
St Margaret's CE Junior School, Rainham

A Smile For Me

Learning about me,
Is as simple as simple can be.
I love having fun,
And laughing with everyone.
But the thing I love most in a mood,
Is not an object nor food.
It is the slightest thing that sets me free,
From sadness for eternity.
A simple smile,
Can travel miles.
Faster than the sound on a guitar,
Faster than a motorbike or a car.
It is not the effort,
That gives me comfort.
But the pleasure it has done,
Before my day has begun.

Mia Colgate (10)
St Margaret's CE Junior School, Rainham

The Unforgiving Stream

There once was an eel,
The eel lived in a river,
The eel wanted to go on a journey,
Sometimes the river was muddy,
Sometimes the eel had to fight strong currents,
Sometimes the river was calm,
Sometimes quiet,
Sometimes it was crowded and the eel got stressed out,
Sometimes the eel felt down due to the coldness,
In the summer there were nice, warm, comforting rivers,
Is this just an eel or is it a stranded thought inside my mind?

Julia Piwowar (9)
St Margaret's CE Junior School, Rainham

This Is Me

T ikTok obsessed, dancing queen,
H elpful daughter and nearly a teen.
I keep up with the latest fashion,
S kateboarding is my passion!

I nsane obsession with cute, fluffy guinea pigs,
S illiness and fun had with different wigs.

M otivated, loving and always trying my best,
E very day living life like a quest.

Lydie Morley (11)
St Margaret's CE Junior School, Rainham

Businessman

B usy making stocks go up
U sing ultimate techniques
S mart people working with me
I t's amazing when the stocks shoot up
N o one is ever sad when we all work together
E stimating how low the stocks will fall or how high they shoot up
S acrificing my time to get stocks up and help people
S killed people are the best
M agical minds are amazing to raise stocks
A secondary manager helps if I am sick
N ifty people are who I love to hire.

Dylan Mudzinganyama (10)
St Patrick's Catholic Primary School, Birmingham

Me!

I am Michal from Birmingham
I like to listen to Michael Jackson
I like my friends at school
I play football with them at break
I have a brother called Eryk
I love Eryk's friends too
I like to play Fortnite with them
I love to read books but I love my family in Poland more
I like all my teachers and school and especially all my friends in Year Five
My favourite thing to do is to play football with my family and uncle
So now you know, all about me!

Michal Smunczinski (10)
St Patrick's Catholic Primary School, Birmingham

The Rainy Days And Life

R ainy days are boring
A nd I always get soaked in the rain
I wish my friends could be here for company
N ever has there been such bad weather like this
Y ou should never shower before you go out in the rain.

D igging holes in the hot weather is exhausting
A pples are healthy and good for you
Y awning is a good feeling
S now is fun to play in.

Gabriela Lisiecka (10)

St Patrick's Catholic Primary School, Birmingham

My Favourite...

D oing stuff with my family
E verybody puts a smile on my face
L aughing in the sun is always fun
I like playing with all my friends
G ummy bears are good in your mouth
H appiness is being free
T ag is my favourite game to play
F risbee is the best
U sually I don't like spiders or bugs
L emon and honey makes me better.

Jozef Rosaupan (9)
St Patrick's Catholic Primary School, Birmingham

Christmas Time

C hristmas, a time to celebrate
H aving fun with friends and family
R eceiving gifts from people I love
I nteracting with loved ones
S itting together and listening to stories
T imes to think about precious moments
M aking gifts with family and friends
A nother happy moment with my family
S inging carol songs with the ones I love.

Ayomiposi Aderinkola (9)
St Patrick's Catholic Primary School, Birmingham

Mermaids And Life

M ay is the best month
E veryone should treat people the way they like
to be treated.
R ain helps flowers grow.
M ako Mermaids is the best thing to watch on
Netflix.
A ll of us should help people if they are sad.
I ndia is a beautiful country
D ays of the week, spellings are easy to write
S undays people go to church.

Nadia Adams (9)
St Patrick's Catholic Primary School, Birmingham

My Acrostic

B olts are made to hold machines
O lives are a topping on pizza,
L evitation means flying high,
T ime is when you wake up for school,

P laying is having fun,
L ong is when something is tall, like me
A pples are fruit to eat and be healthy
Y elling is when you're loud, and this is my poem.

Hubert Rzepecki (9)
St Patrick's Catholic Primary School, Birmingham

I Am A Korean

I am a Korean
I grew up in Pohang

I can sing along to BTS songs
But I can't watch Harry Potter films without subtitles

In England,
there are more unfamiliar things than familiar
I am still not used to the scenery of Birmingham

However,
everything is very precious to me

I love these things as a part of me.

Jihu Kim (10)
St Patrick's Catholic Primary School, Birmingham

My Name Is...

M y name is Minsa
Y oghurt is delicious.

N ow I am ten on January 24th
A chocolate ice cream is yummy to eat in summer
M aroon and pink are my favourite colours
E aster is in April.

I ndoors is where I love to play
S lime is fun to play with with friends.

Minsa Mumtaz (10)
St Patrick's Catholic Primary School, Birmingham

Be Happy

My name is Kyah and I have curly hair
I am very kind and I like to share
I love to be happy every day
I make people smile in my own special way
If you are feeling down, never frown
I will always be around
I love my family and friends
I really love school, I think it's cool
So always be happy in every way
And make someone smile today.

Kyah Coward (9)
St Patrick's Catholic Primary School, Birmingham

Me And My Emotions

I'm as calm as the sea and as warm as the sun,
I love art as much as I love my family,
I'm as kind as a flower,
I love baking like I love myself,
I'm as stretchable as a gymnast,
I'm as clever as a brand-new mirror,
I'm a book lover as much as I love food,
I'm as calm as the waves and as still as a rock.

Alicia Anderson Nyafre (10)
St Patrick's Catholic Primary School, Birmingham

Wild Dreams And Me

This is me,
A boy in Year 5,
I'm Joshua,
I love my mom, dad and sister Hannah,
Being a gamer and making money and achieving is my dream
My sister Hannah makes me laugh and cheers me up,
A bigger dream is becoming the prime minister,
My favourite thing about me is my work and my art,
Maybe one day,
My dreams will come true.

Joshua Nyika (9)
St Patrick's Catholic Primary School, Birmingham

It's My Birthday

B eing happy, it's my special day
I nviting family and friends
R eady to party
T ime to dance and celebrate
H aving a great time is my desire
D ancing with friends
A nother moment of joy for me
Y ippee! Can't wait for another year.

Aymoide Aderinkola (9)
St Patrick's Catholic Primary School, Birmingham

Hobbies And Personality

H andwriting is fun to do, but hurts my hand.
O nly drawing is what I like the most,
B y practising, I get better at art.
B eing better at sports is my dream.
I ce is nice to eat,
E verybody in class knows me,
S till I secretly draw.

Arianne Mirador (10)
St Patrick's Catholic Primary School, Birmingham

What Makes Me Happy

A big fat hug or hot chocolate in my mug,
Playing with my friend or maybe family,
When you see me smile you know my mood,
Or maybe lots of food,
Having birthday parties and sometimes eating Smarties,
Watching football with my family,
And that's what makes me happy.

Ayomide Banjo (10)
St Patrick's Catholic Primary School, Birmingham

My Football Future

I had a sense that the park was suddenly empty
A pair of Adidas Predators was near the football net
I want to be as good as Messi and Ronaldo
When I slowly put the Predators on
I am as fast as a bolting, thunderous storm
Somehow I feel a great, magical light inside of me.

Natan Haile (9)
St Patrick's Catholic Primary School, Birmingham

Journey Ahead

Become the best
Using my brain, no fear to rest
Inserting my cash into my bag
So rich, not trying to brag
Never gonna give up, when I'm with my friends
Exciting journey, make sure it never ends
Stay with the big bucks
I will never leave the big bucks.

Marzuq Akinbami (10)
St Patrick's Catholic Primary School, Birmingham

Mexico

My heart is Mexican
Enjoying fiesta all the time
Christmas has piñatas
I invite you to experience those colours, flavours and sounds
Once, twice or many other times.

Santiago Ernesto Salinas-Mejia (9)
St Patrick's Catholic Primary School, Birmingham

My Brother

I enjoy playing games but my brother is more fun
He always makes me laugh
I play with him every day
This is why I love him
Because he is always fair.

Kaiden Graham (9)
St Patrick's Catholic Primary School, Birmingham

Peaceful

Peaceful is birds chirping right next to you.
Peaceful is you smiling because the sun is setting and the ocean is glowing golden.
Peaceful is feeling warm inside.
Peaceful is a starry night watching the stars.
Peaceful is watching fireworks while eating food.
Peaceful is playing on the beach with your friends.
Peaceful is listening to calm music and lying down.
Peaceful is being with friends and family on a nice day and playing.
Peaceful is having everyone you know and love come over to your house.
Peaceful is going to the park with everyone you know and having a party.
Peaceful is having a picnic with your parents and siblings.
Peaceful is playing in the snow and playing in the autumn leaves
Peaceful is being with family.

Georgie Waterhouse-Davey (9)
St Peter's CE First School, Marchington

Happy

Happy is the gentle, calm sea on the windy beach.
Happy is when I am with my family.
Happy is when I am with my guinea pig.
Happy is when I am in my bed reading a book.
Happy is when I am with my friends in the nice, warm sun.
Happy is when I am building a snowman with my sisters.
Happy is when I am with animals because it is nice and peaceful.
Happy is when I see a rainbow because it is pretty and colourful.
Happy is when I am with my nan and grandad because it is nice to see them.
Happy is when I am in the nice, cold sea in the summer.
Happy is when I am at school because I get to see my friends.
Happy is when I am swimming because I can learn to swim.

Bella Darlington (7)
St Peter's CE First School, Marchington

Quiet

Quiet is when you go to the sea when you relax in the sun, if it is too cold to go just stay at home and stay by the fireplace.
Quiet is when you see a tree swaying gently.
Quiet is when you go into a swimming pool, try a slide, it will be nice and cool, if you are scared just hop in, you will be safe.
Quiet is when you are in your bed sleeping quietly but no snoring, but sometimes you have bad dreams.
Quiet is when you see a rainbow, it is raining but that is okay, it is sunny and beautiful colours, so nice and quiet.

Annabel Langston (8)
St Peter's CE First School, Marchington

Calmness

Calm is eating a warm tasty pizza
I feel it melting in my mouth
And my cat using me as a climbing frame.
Calm is watching the bright yellow
As a leopard sun fades into a calm dark navy blue.
Calm is walking up the steep stairs
And I sleepily doze away into my soft comfy bed.
Calm is making a giant snowman
And because all the sticks are buried in soft fluffy snow
I used my mum's wooden spoons.

Seth Hallam
St Peter's CE First School, Marchington

Happy

I am happy
When I play with my sister,
She makes funny noises
And has a loud cackle
And we play games.

I am happy
When I am at school
And do lots of work
And play with my friends.

I am happy
When it is my birthday
And I get presents and parties
And friends come for cake.

I am happy
In thunderstorms and in rainbows,
The noise of the thunder,
The flash of the lightning
And the beautiful colours of the rainbow after.

Caitlin Davies (8)
St Peter's CE First School, Marchington

Peaceful

Peaceful is when I get into my bed and I read my book.
Peaceful is when I'm on the beach with the calm sun shining on me.
Peaceful is having a nice cuddle with nanny and mummy.
Peaceful is listening to nice singing.
Peaceful is spending time with family.
Peaceful is nice to go to school and spend time with friends.
Peaceful is loving others and especially Mummy, Daddy and Liv.

Orla Stanley (7)

St Peter's CE First School, Marchington

Peaceful

P eaceful is calm
E verybody likes to feel calm
A calm time
C alm is peaceful
E very day feels calm
F eel calm today
U nderstand peaceful
L ove peaceful.

I love peaceful
S ee, peaceful is calm.

M e is calm
E verybody can feel calm.

Archie Birkinshaw (6)
St Peter's CE First School, Marchington

Peaceful

The sound of a horse's hooves
Constantly hitting the stones
Is all to be heard
With birds
And your hands on the cold reins
That makes me peaceful.

The sound of a book's pages
Being turned over
Is all to be heard
Is what makes me peaceful.

The purring of cats
With soft, comfortable fur
All over their peaceful faces
Is all to be heard
And makes me peaceful.

Alice
St Peter's CE First School, Marchington

Calm

When I am calm
I think about being under a rainbow
It is shimmering, shining and sparkling above me.
When I am calm
I think about being able to fly and soaring through the sky.
When I am calm
I think about sitting on a fluffy cloud in the lovely blue sky.

Eliza Ede (7)
St Peter's CE First School, Marchington

Happiness

Happiness is when I'm walking my dogs and pulling up at my favourite restaurant.
Happiness is being in the snow and being at the beach making sandcastles.
Happiness is looking at a rainbow.
Happiness is 11:59 at night on Christmas Eve.
Happiness always makes my day.

Eddy Coates (8)
St Peter's CE First School, Marchington

Happy

Happy is when you go to the park.
Happy is when you see your family and friends.
Happy is when you have a teddy bear picnic.
Happy is when you see a rainbow above your head.
Happy is when you help somebody in need.
Happy is when you get a new pet and you play with it.

Amelia Share (8)
St Peter's CE First School, Marchington

Happy

Happy is when I am playing with my brothers at the farm
Happy is when I think of tractors in the field in my head
Happy is when I am walking my dogs down the lanes
Happy is when I am with my sheep and family
Happy is when I am doing my favourite sport - swimming.

William Buxton (8)
St Peter's CE First School, Marchington

Happy

Happy is the warmth of the sun.
Happy is looking for a rainbow up in the sky, if I don't get one, I sigh.
Happy is getting presents on your birthday.
Happy is going on holiday.
Happy is feeling the waves.
Happy is going to the park and having fun.

Elsie Powell (6)
St Peter's CE First School, Marchington

Excited

Excited is when my birthday comes
I run downstairs to fetch my mum waiting in the living room
To my surprise, my brother hides in between my mum and dad!
I will open the presents without him!
He jumps out and shouts, "No!"

Florence Orme
St Peter's CE First School, Marchington

Happy

At my birthday, I get lots and lots of lovely gifts.
We decorate my party and it looks amazing.
When my friends come, it looks better.
We have cake, it is great.
When it is time to leave, I open my presents, they are great!

Elsie Handy (7)
St Peter's CE First School, Marchington

Relaxed

Relaxed is snuggling with my mum.
Relaxed is my beauty sleep when I wake up in the morning.
Relaxed is cuddling with my dog.
Relaxed is stroking Lucy, I really miss her.
I love relaxing.

Vivienne Walker (8)
St Peter's CE First School, Marchington

What Colour Am I Feeling?

Anger is red like hot chilli
Happy is yellow like the bright sun
Sad is blue like the pouring rain
Bored is grey like a cloudy day.

Henry Carter (7)

St Peter's CE First School, Marchington

Happy

Happy is music flowing through my head.
Happy is family and friends.
Happy is TV with family.
Happy is amazing.
Happy is my favourite feeling.

Erin Gildart (7)
St Peter's CE First School, Marchington

Happy

School is a happy place.
Don't cry, happy is a good feeling.
When you are sad, happy saves the day
So the sadness runs away.

Bobby Lowman
St Peter's CE First School, Marchington

My Favourite

I love koalas.
They are so cute and cuddly.
I collect stuffed toy ones.
My dad says I have at least twenty of them.
I want to see a real one in a eucalyptus tree in Australia.
But I don't want to see scary spiders while I am there!
I have a cheeky, younger brother.
He likes my koalas too.
I let him hug all of them except one.
Brucie. He is my special koala.
He is my favourite.

Eleanor Kilburn (8)
Stanley Park Junior School, Carshalton

This Is Me!

India is where I'm from
I love everyone in my family but mostly my mom.
I am polite, kind, and generous
Some would also say that I'm super adventurous.

There's badminton, my favourite sport
My height is four foot eleven, that's not short!
I'm good at maths and many other subjects
However, I am not a fan of crawling and flying
insects.

I do cross-stitch, it's quite hard work
But in the end, it turns out to be beautiful artwork!
I play the whistling flute and practise every day
My favourite song is Lazy Sunday.

My hair is super long
It is hard to wash, takes a lot of water and hands
that are strong.
Wherever I go my hair is the topic of conversation
Everyone asks for hair care suggestions.

Too many friends to list or count
What can I say, it's such a big amount?
This poem has a few things about me like a collection of photos
An autobiography is what I will next compose.

Niyati Pareek (11)

Stanley Park Junior School, Carshalton

This Is Me!

T asty treats baking in the oven
H arry Potter - biggest fan ever!
I love my crazy family to the moon and back
S ketching, drawing and painting everywhere.

I play the piano every day
S parky and Snowy are my cuddly cats.

M usic by Adele makes me happy
E njoy climbing with Molly every Friday night!

Bonnie Stubberfield (11)
Stanley Park Junior School, Carshalton

Get To Know Me

I'm the sunniest person you could ever meet,
Some people say I smell so sweet.
I like to make my friends laugh,
I've known them since before I was a giraffe!
Art is one of my favourite things to do,
Though I am still learning how to tie my shoes.
I dream to be a pop star one day,
And did you know my middle name is Fay?

Sadie Bridge (8)
Stanley Park Junior School, Carshalton

I Am...

Sometimes I am shy
Sometimes I speak
Sometimes I am strong
Sometimes I am weak.

Sometimes I am right
Sometimes I am wrong
Sometimes I understand lyrics
Sometimes I enjoy the song.

Sometimes I am in death
Sometimes I am breath
Sometimes I am 'you'
Sometimes I am 'me'.

Zheng Nan Lee (9)
Stanley Park Junior School, Carshalton

Me

T hinking like my big old brother
H uddling with my pillow or other
I n my room with a lot of Lego
S aving time to play the piano.

I am funny and an animal lover
S till, red is my favourite colour.

M aths is my favourite subject
E nding this with great respect.

Gaurava Gunarathna (7)
Stanley Park Junior School, Carshalton

Feelings

Feelings are like colours
Not quite like the others
Every emotion
Stops in their motion
Sometimes I'm sad
And sometimes I'm glad
Gazing at the feelings
That makes it more appealing
Every colour is a sentimental meaning
Makes me think of dreaming
What are the other colours that will leave me beaming?

Sophia Injore (10)
Stanley Park Junior School, Carshalton

All About Me

My name is Ethan and I play video games
I eat some pizza in-between frames
Although it's bad for you, it is exceptionally scrumptious
On the tip of your tongue, I like to munch first
I go for a walk with my bike
With one pedal short, but I like
Playing football on the fields
Like a kite that reveals
The sun.

Ethan Philippou (8)
Stanley Park Junior School, Carshalton

Mia

I am going to talk to you about Mia!

M stands for the madness and magical games I make with my friends, and macaroni because it is my favourite food!
I stands for imagination and ideas I use to write stories!
A stands for active, I never sit still, and adventurous because I like excitement!

Mia Injore (8)

Stanley Park Junior School, Carshalton

Fantastic Me!

F abulous me,
A rtistic and musical,
N inja superstar,
T rainer at kung fu,
A ctive leaner,
S porty kid,
T ypically seven!
I nspiring and loving,
C aring and creative.

M arvellous friend,
E xtraordinary me!

Kai Lopez (7)
Stanley Park Junior School, Carshalton

This Is Me

T all am I
H andy, I am told
I love using my head
S tan will always be my name.

I ncreasing brain power every day
S ci-fi is my favourite genre.

M akes fantastic drawings
E xcellent at swimming.

Stanley Brooks
Stanley Park Junior School, Carshalton

This Is Me

T houghtful is my spotlight,
H elpful is my talent,
I ndependent,
S elfless,

I maginative and creative,
S ensible,

M agical in my own way,
E nthusiastic.

This is a poem about me!

Swara Deshpande (9)
Stanley Park Junior School, Carshalton

I Love Nature

I love the gentle breeze,
The brightness of the sun,
Nature is so much at ease,
She is so much fun.

If you love nature as much as I do,
Please do your bit too,
Conserve nature, its fate relies on you,
Save her,
Save our nature!

Lily Galligan (8)
Stanley Park Junior School, Carshalton

This Is Me

S uper good at gaming
A mazing at reading
M aths is one thing I am good at
U pset that I don't have a pet
E lephants are one of my favourite animals
L oud noises are the worst.

Samuel Appiah-Ampofo (9)
Stanley Park Junior School, Carshalton

Newcastle The Great

Black and white is my team,
When we score you'll hear me scream.
They score a goal from afar,
It goes right in off the bar.
One goal,
Two goal,
Three goal,
Four.
Can you hear my mighty roar?

Kaycie Stevens (10)
Stanley Park Junior School, Carshalton

About Jenni

J oyful as a mermaid
E nergetic like a car
N umerous friends
N utty as a fruit cake
I nteresting like a museum.

Jennifer Reeves (8)

Stanley Park Junior School, Carshalton

Poetry

My head is round
It can be found
On top of my body.
I have a brain
But it's in pain
When I read poetry.

Ryan Halsey (10)
Stanley Park Junior School, Carshalton

I Am Elliot

I have a watch with buttons

A nd I am eight years old
M ight get a prize, I don't know!

E xcept that I am maybe too polite
L iked, smart, happy, helpful and
L oved by my family and friends
I want to be a librarian when I'm
O lder or a famous, happy footballer
T hat's me

Y ahoo!
A nd here we go again (my dad farts)
Y uck! And he says he's perfect (not)!

Elliot Brailsford (8)
Tarbert Academy, Tarbert

The Person I Am

The person I am is a different type,
Kind of a dissimilar hype,
Following dreams and ambitions is not my thing,
But they attract my mind like a ding,
My friends and family's support grows strong,
And I know they're never wrong,
Though I am still thinking of what I want to become,
It's not an easy choice to choose from,
I am equal to many combinations,
But none of them fulfil my frustrations,
I try my hardest to achieve my goals,
To attain all souls,
The person I am is the person I want to be,
Beautiful as a blossom tree.

Areeba Saqib
The Bulmershe School, Woodley

This Is Me

Kyra
Is committed, smart, helpful and independent.
Daughter of Lynne and David Williams, her wonderful parents.
Who loves singing, dancing and helping younger children.
Who hates liars, global warming and racism.
Who dreams of being a rockstar, helping children's charities and making a difference in the world.
Who fears being left alone anywhere, jellyfish and picking up cats.
Who would like to see Australia, all bad diseases gone forever and a unicorn.
Who is determined to be a rockstar, a charity helper and live the best life she can.
Who values kindness, honesty and trustworthiness.
Who is proud of her dogs Tico and Zeus, my friends and my beloved family.
Who lives in Merthyr Tydfil.

This is me,
Kyra Myr Williams.

Kyra Williams (10)
Twynyrodyn Community School, Twynyrodyn

This Is Me

Izzy
Is kind, creative, bossy and bubbly.
Daughter of Sarah and Gethyn Morgan, my wonderful parents.
Who loves animals, films, dance and holidays.
Who hates the kind of people who discriminate against others, the effect of suicide and of racism.
Who dreams of going to the Maldives, travelling the world with people she loves and being a teacher or a fashion designer.
Who fears spiders, the sea, drowning and clowns.
Who would like to see a Cirque du Soleil show once again, to meet Tom Holland and watch many more Broadway shows.
Who is determined to get a good job, a successful career and to do well throughout school.
Who values passion, creativity and love.
Who is proud of going parasailing, adopting dogs and being Welsh.

Who lives in a small town called Merthyr Tydfil in Wales.

This is me!
Isabelle Morgan.

Izzy Morgan (11)
Twynyrodyn Community School, Twynyrodyn

This Is Me

Zac
Is kind, caring, fun and energetic.
Son of Emma Keen, my wonderful mother.
Who loves rugby, science and maths.
Who hates death, racism and the effects of war.
Who dreams of winning the Nobel Prize,
graduating from university and becoming a
physicist.
Who fears the world ending, artificial intelligence
taking over and the sun exploding.
Who would like to see Isaac Newton, the King of
Sweden and the Eiffel Tower.
Who is determined to get into a university, get a
PHD and challenge myself as much as I can.
Who values humour, love and friendship.
Who is proud of his heritage, knowledge and
family.
Who lives in Merthyr Tydfil, a small, lovely town
packed with history.

This is me
Zac Keen.

Zac Keen (11)
Twynyrodyn Community School, Twynyrodyn

This Is Me

Elliot
Is kind caring and fun.
Relative of Rachel and Nathan Williams, my parents.
Who loves football, family and dogs.
Who hates people who discriminate against others, racism and onions.
Who dreams of meeting Mohammed Salah, ending all war and ending racism.
Who fears war, dolls and killer whales.
Who would like to see the Grand Canyon, Mohamed Salah, the Great Pyramid of Giza.
Who is determined to become better at football.
Who values my family and my friends.
Who is proud of jumping off a thirty-foot cliff into a lake, going on a rollercoaster that went 105 feet high in the air then dropped.
Who lives Wales
In Merthyr Tydfil.

This is me
Elliot Jack Williams.

Elliot Williams (10)
Twynyrodyn Community School, Twynyrodyn

This Is Me

Lily
Is hardworking, loving, committed and cheerful,
Daughter of Nick and Jodie Etheridge, my wonderful parents.
Who loves all of my family friends and football.
Who hates the effects of suicide, people in the wrong and racism.
Who dreams of being an actor or designer.
Who fears death, of myself or a loved one, and world war.
Who would like to see Tanner Buchanan, William Zakba and Mohamed Salah.
Who is determined to get a good job and career.
Who values loyalty compassion honesty kindness and respect.
Who is proud of family, being good at football and being respectful.
Who lives in Twyn, Merthyr Tydfil in Wales, a lovely place.

This is me
Lily Etheridge.

Lily Etheridge (10)
Twynyrodyn Community School, Twynyrodyn

This Is Me

Jacob
Who is creative, honest, reliable and funny.
Who is related to Leanne and Raith Greenway, my wonderful parents.
Who loves ants, plants, family and my cat.
Who hates suicide, Covid and global warming.
Who dreams of being a marine biologist, seeing all the types of fish and having an ant colony.
Who fears death, dark rooms and being alone.
Who would like to see people merry, smiling and having fun.
Who is determined to make people happy, have a good job and do well in school.
Who values friendship, love and life.
Who is proud of his family, friends and teacher.
Who lives in Merthyr Tydfil, a lovely town in Wales.

This is me
Jacob Greenway.

Jacob Greenway (11)
Twynyrodyn Community School, Twynyrodyn

This Is Me

Jack
Is happy, funny, artistic and sporty.
Son of Elena and Bleddyn.
Who loves Liverpool, football, family, video games and my dog Oscar.
Who hates Covid and swimming.
Who dreams of becoming a pilot and a football player and going to France.
Who fears claustrophobia.
Who would like to see Covid end, be successful, see global warming end and to meet Diogo Jota.
Who is determined to have a fantastic life.
Who values to be funny and smart.
Who lives in Merthyr Tydfil, a town in South Wales.
I live by a massive park called Thomas Town Park and massive black gates blocking people from entering my estate.

This is me
Jack Richards.

Jack Richards (10)
Twynyrodyn Community School, Twynyrodyn

This Is Me

Oliver
Is kind, caring, helpful and smart.
Son of Sarah and Colin Powney, my wonderful parents.
Who loves football, school, video games and fun.
Who hates racism, bullying and the effects of suicide.
Who dreams of happiness, a good life and a successful career.
Who fears war, death and depression of me or a loved one.
Who would like to see the Maldives, Dubai and a professional footballer.
Who is determined to work hard, be happy and committed.
Who values love, family and friends.
Who is proud of passion, heritage and mathematic ability.
Who lives in Merthyr Tydfil, a lovely town in South Wales.

This is me
Oliver Powney.

Oliver Powney (11)
Twynyrodyn Community School, Twynyrodyn

This Is Me

Mali
Is friendly, kind, helpful, and honest.
Relative of Caryl and Richard Parry, who are my amazing parents.
Who loves gymnastics, school, family, and pets.
Who hates people littering, racism and Covid.
Who dreams of being a zoologist or a professional gymnast.
Who fears spiders and roller coasters.
Who would like to see Katelyn Ohashi, happy people in the world and the end of racism.
Who is determined to stick at every skill in gymnastics.
Who values kindness, honesty and friendliness.
Who is proud of drawings, achievements and making friends in a new school.
Who lives in Merthyr Tydfil.

This is me
Mali Gwen Parry.

Mali Parry (9)
Twynyrodyn Community School, Twynyrodyn

This Is Me

Amelie
Is kind, organised, smart and helpful.
Daughter of Emma and Ryan Burrows, sister of Ethan Burrows.
Who loves my bunny, my parents and dancing.
Who hates racism, death and thoughts of suicide.
Who dreams of a successful career, graduating and becoming a hairdresser.
Who fears spiders, death of a loved one and getting kidnapped.
Who would like to see New York, Malta and Turkey.
Who is determined to finish my work and to be a better friend.
Who values forgiveness, honesty and trust.
Who is proud of my heritage and my culture.
Who lives in Merthyr Tydfil.

This is me
Amelie Burrows.

Amelie Burrows (11)
Twynyrodyn Community School, Twynyrodyn

This Is Me

Amber
Is confident, happy, smart and funny.
Relative of Kimberley and Michael Smart, my wonderful parents.
Who loves singing, video games and animals.
Who hates war, suicide and inequality.
Who dreams of becoming a vet, going to a concert and world peace.
Who fears global warming, death and heights.
Who would like to see Hawaii, a tiger and a panda.
Who is determined to finish work, become a vet and stop violence.
Who values kindness, honesty and courage.
Who is proud of Wales, the NHS and myself.
Who lives in Merthyr Tydfil Wales in Britain.

This is me.
Amber Smart.

Amber Smart (11)
Twynyrodyn Community School, Twynyrodyn

I'm Unique

I am unique, I am perfect the way I am,
I have a weird art technique but I'll be sure to give you a hand.
I am crazy, I am clumsy but I'll understand for sure.
I love to craft and draw and sew,
Don't forget about resin and clay,
I could do those all day.
I like to be creative and give people ideas
But I'll often get left out and that nearly leaves me in tears.
I've had seventeen pets and even more in my dreams.
If I get selected to be a leader I'll create a supportive team.
I've donated a lot to charity to help people in need.
I'm creative and fun and that's about me!

Maisie-Lee Parker-Keetley (11)
Washingborough Academy, Washingborough

The Ballet Star - Bella

A ballet person, a ballet person
The most famous of them all
But who could it be? Oh, who could it be?
The most famous of them all
Oh, who could it be? Oh, could it be Bella?
The best in her class
You or we or I should find out
How is this possible?
She's come from Australia and come to England!
Should we watch her perform?
The judges will sit down to watch
This amazing performance
As it is finished everyone stands up and
A round of applause to Isabella!
The best ballet star
Oh yes, I've found my favourite one!

Isabella-Rae Rosario Symonds (9)
Washingborough Academy, Washingborough

Me

My name is Noah, I'm not lazy
I play football because I'm crazy
You might know I'm 11
I like finding people
My friends are kind
I like my teacher, they are nice
I like pies
I don't like being alone
I should have known that I will be getting homework
Because I'm not prepared for this
But here I am doing it,
I'm sitting down, thinking my next word
It's hard this year
Because SATs are coming up
It's just around the corner
That's me.

Noah Rousseau (11)
Washingborough Academy, Washingborough

Me, Myself And I

Loving but doubtful.
We're all special but here are some special things about me.
I play the drums as it's very fun.
I like to rhyme and get dirty in the mud and grime.
I dance in the rain, it washes away the pain.
I'm ten years old so I'm proud and bold.
Blue is my favourite colour though I like many others.
2 is my favourite number but meeting two new people is even funner.
That is my poem, my name is Lucca,
Hope you enjoyed it and weren't annoyed by it.

Lucca Brackenbury (10)
Washingborough Academy, Washingborough

All About Me!

My name is Jack,
My favourite colour is black.
My age is eleven,
Eating Domino's pizza is my heaven.
I like to walk my dog,
When feeling energetic, I like to jog.
One of my favourite movies is Avatar,
Also the instrument I play is electric guitar.
A trip to the cinema gets me excited,
Like watching Ronaldo play for Manchester United.
I'm funny and caring, like a good friend,
I hope you kept reading right to the end!

Jack Austin (11)
Washingborough Academy, Washingborough

Just Like Nature

L ike a miniature oak tree - solid, dependable and always there for my family.
I am a tornado when angry - tearing up everything in my path, but I am the snow falling from the sky to bring happiness to everyone around me.
L ike leaves in autumn slowly fluttering to the ground without a care in the world.
L onging to be an elegant swan but realising that they're not perfect under the water.
Y et perfect for my family!

Lilly Hyde (11)
Washingborough Academy, Washingborough

A Cup Of Tea

My name is Ollie, this poem is about me
I am 11 years old and I drink lots of tea.

I love to read, I like fiction and fact books
The last fact book I read was all about a duck.

I made it into the school football team
I was really happy, I was living the dream.

I like my friends and family too
Can't wait to go to Branston School.

Now you have heard all about me
I'm off to make a cup of tea.

Ollie Gurnhill (11)
Washingborough Academy, Washingborough

I Believe In Myself

I believe in myself,
In this world I want to be many things,
I can't let anyone's envy control what I think,
I like making friends and communicating with others,
Anything I put my mind to,
I know that's what I can do,
I believe in myself.

With God I know I can be anything,
I can be shy but also kind,
This is who I am,
And nothing will change that,
I believe in myself.

Maya Scott (10)
Washingborough Academy, Washingborough

Dream Big

I dream big and reach for the stars
I'll make mistakes and learn from them
I'll be the kind kid
I won't be afraid to stand out in a crowd
Because I remember that I am special
I am proud of myself
I am lucky to be me and I am amazing!

S pecial because I am unique to other people
E xcellent friend
B rave for trying new things.

Sebastian Buck (10)
Washingborough Academy, Washingborough

All About Me

Hello, my name is Harry, I'm a massive Xbox fan
My favourite game is Fortnite, it really annoys my nan!

I like my Sunday dinners, they are really rather filling
I also like lots of sleep and I spend my weekends chilling!

I like to see my mates, we have a lot of fun
We run around playing football until the day is done.

Harry Edison (10)
Washingborough Academy, Washingborough

About Me!

My name is Harry, I am ten years old,
I am kind and caring, or so I am told.
I like riding horses, her name is Bella,
It's fun unless it's raining without an umbrella.
My favourite hobby is cooking, I'm a whizz at chocolate cake,
But sometimes I get cross when the oven doesn't bake.

Harry Chapman (10)
Washingborough Academy, Washingborough

All About Me!

A is for amazing dancer
I is for intelligent swimming
M is for magical reader
E is for elegant ballet
E is for exquisite work

M is for magnificent helper
A is for approachable friend
Y is for yummy food Mom makes.

Aimee May Patrick (11)
Washingborough Academy, Washingborough

Life In Leo Land

Leo is my name
Football is my game
Man United is my team
To play for them is the dream
And when they score I scream
School is where my love for maths starts
Which helps me at home adding up my darts
I have two brothers who are very crazy
And two dogs just as lazy.

Leo Knibbs (10)
Washingborough Academy, Washingborough

Me

I am brave as a lion
I am strong as a gorilla
I am as fast as lightning
I am as cool as a cucumber
I am as quiet as a turtle
I am sweet as sugar
I am as friendly as the brightest star
I am tough as nails
I am proud as a peacock.

Ollie Spraggins (11)
Washingborough Academy, Washingborough

Ruben

R acing across that muddy field after that ball
U nbelievable shots making my eye twitch
B arging past those who stop me
E leven people working as one team
N ike boots on my feet hoping to hit a score in a streak.

Ruben Robinson (10)
Washingborough Academy, Washingborough

A Poem About Myself

I am special,
I am me, I can
Be who I want to be

I can be sensitive
I can be shy or
I can be a thunderbolt
In the sky

I will laugh
I will joke but
Sometimes I can be a
Pain in the throat.

Phoebe Robinson (10)
Washingborough Academy, Washingborough

All About Me!

K ind and caring
A mazing at gaming
I have lots of tolerance
R eally like pizza
A mazing at motorbiking
N ow this poem will end.

Kairan Cox
Washingborough Academy, Washingborough

When I'm Older

When I'm older I want to slam dunk and play in the NBA,
Being competitive and playing with my team,
But I also want to save lives and be a doctor,
Healing people and giving them a second chance,
But I also want to dig up new species of dinosaur,
Enriching our knowledge of the Earth and where we came from,
But I also want to protect the trees, bees and seas,
Making sure that climate change doesn't ruin us.

It seems like I'll be busy when I'm older.

Nihal Babbra
Westbrook Primary School, Heston

This Is Me

Born in LA hospital, first thing I see,
The ugly doctor's teeth glaring right at me,
I howled and scowled until back home,
Don't blame me, I'm just an innocent gnome.

Years later, now just wait till you see,
I'm older and wiser, slurping bubble tea,
Favourite cuisines are sushi and Margherita,
I'm just so fond of hot, cheesy pizza.

I'm a lightning dash both in football and rugby,
I score goals and tries, all the coaches love me,
Challenge me, it's utter humiliation,
I cause my opponents total devastation.

I manage my studies like Jurgen Klopp,
Academic sweat, hard work pays off,
My speciality is geography,
Room 303, the ideal place to be.

My dad's Argentinian my mother's Francais,
My hair is so messy, it's just a wave,

My eyes are chestnut, I've got a nine pack,
Best swimmer in the year.

I'm helpful, kind, caring and honest.
This is me.

Evo Sulichin (10)
Wetherby Prep School, Marylebone

This Is Me!

I am brave when I'm scared or when my friends are scared,
I like to help my friends when they need it,
I am kind-hearted, easy-going and non-judgemental.
I love playing football and maths because it is close to my heart,
I love to cook and learn new recipes like my dad,
He taught me how to cook my favourite meal which is homemade lasagne.
I make my mum proud when I get on with my sister,
Help her with schoolwork and day-to-day problems.
Inside I can be hard on myself,
When I get a little bit of help from family, friends or teachers.
I get through it and feel happy about myself,
For overcoming the problem.

William Bamford (10)
Ysgol Cei Newydd, Cei Newydd

Computers

Here is a poem about me,
And the thing that makes me happy.
That thing is computers, I bet you'll like them too,
But first let me explain what they are and what
they do.

Computers have been around since 1871,
But these days we use them for help and fun.
Originally built with metal and electricity,
Computers have changed ever so greatly.
Whether it be for work, help or even just for fun,
The computer is great and gets the job done.

Computers are full of many cool features,
Like Word or Excel, they're great for teachers!
Computers can help when you're having a dreadful
day,
You can watch a film or YouTube to make you feel
okay.
Computers come in many shapes and sizes,
Just like many other amazing devices.

So that's the thing. The thing that makes me smile,
My love for them goes on for more than a mile.
Computers are fragile, so treat them with care,
And when I say I love them, I mean it, I swear!

Jason Yates (11)
Ysgol Cei Newydd, Cei Newydd

My Colourful Rainbow

In my colourful rainbow I have,
Red, which is mad and furious,
Which only shows up if someone is mean,
Or I mess up my work,
The only way to stop him is to take a deep breath,
And have happy thoughts.

In my colourful rainbow I have,
Orange, which is always hungry,
As hungry as a starving wolf,
He shows up in the morning at breakfast time,
His mouth is always drooling,
Because of how hungry he is.

In my colourful rainbow I have,
Yellow! My favourite because of how happy he always is,
Always has a wide happy smile,
As wide as a yummy, yellow banana,
Shining with happiness like a bright sun in summer.

And this is my rainbow full of emotions,
Some good, some bad, but they all matter,
They are the ones that describe me the most.

Olivia Zamorowska (11)
Ysgol Cei Newydd, Cei Newydd

I Am Me!

My name is Sapphira,
From the sapphire gem,
It takes millions of years to find them.

I don't like mean people,
As they make me sad,
It's best to be kind,
Rather than cruel and bad.

My favourite food is hard to say,
But I like to eat at least three times a day.

I fly on my holidays to Malta and France,
I ride on the horse to trot and prance,
I play games non-stop,
But when I lose I get into a big strop.

I love my friends and family too,
If I lost them I would not know what to do.

Sapphira Gibbons (11)
Ysgol Cei Newydd, Cei Newydd

This Is Me

This is me and I am Josh,
And I like to power wash,
My dad's truck, it's squeaky clean,
And full of cans of baked beans.
We sit sometimes on the tailgate,
And watch the stars, I think it's great.
I love to talk all about farms,
Ravenseat and all its charms,
The Yorkshire farm I think it's great
With their farm dog, her name is Kate.
Lots of kids and cows and sheep,
Tony the pony, he likes to sleep,
In his barn, all tucked up warm,
When Clemmie's not there he feels torn.

Josh Griffiths (11)
Ysgol Cei Newydd, Cei Newydd

Awesome Me

I live in Cei
And like to surf the bay.
When the waves fall,
You'll find me kicking a ball,
With a demon left boot,
Made to shoot!
When it's raining,
You'll find me gaming.
But if the wifi's down,
You'll see me frown.
Play fighting with my brother,
And annoying my mother.
I'm a friendly dude,
And don't like being rude.
I like to help people out,
Whenever they are in doubt.
This is me -
The *awesome* me.

Reuben Hopkins (11)
Ysgol Cei Newydd, Cei Newydd

I Am Me

Hi, my name is Zac,
I like to play attack,
Football is my game,
Trying to score is my aim.

I am age eleven,
I'm also in Year 6,
My favourite subject is maths,
Dividing and subtracting.

Xbox is my thing,
FIFA is what I play,
I also do F1,
Trying to be number one.

I watch TV,
I also like PE,
You can find me on the pitch,
Waiting for my team to make a switch.

Zac Colley (11)
Ysgol Cei Newydd, Cei Newydd

This Is Me

My name is actually Albert but I like to be called Bertie,
When people call me by my given name I tend to get a bit shirty,
I support a football team called Stoke,
My friends laugh and think it's a joke,
When we lose it sends me insane,
But when we win I smile again,
Win or lose I like to play football with my friends,
And try my hardest until the match ends.

Bertie Tilstone (11)
Ysgol Cei Newydd, Cei Newydd

My Baby Sister

My baby sister
Yes she is loud
Blossom of joy
And cheeky too.
Bath time is fun
You can get wet!
So cute and adorable
In her teddy bear suit.
So, I'd like to say thank you for all the joy and fun
Today was fun
Just me and you.
Every day when we are away, I miss you
Reading books, just me and you.
My baby sister.

Layla Davies (10)
Ysgol Cei Newydd, Cei Newydd

Phoenix

P ersonality, which mum says I have bags of.
H ome is where I feel happy.
O utside I happily play on my scooter.
E arly in the morning, I hate getting up.
N ight-time I am the best at getting down.
I ndulging on pickled gherkins is my thing, I could eat jars of the pickle trains.
X box is my time to relax.

Phoenix Slawson (9)
Ysgol Cei Newydd, Cei Newydd

This Is Me

This is me, I play loads of football.
My favourite colour's yellow,
And I like drawing a lot.

This is me, I am super speedy.
My favourite food is pizza,
And I play songs on my guitar.

This is me, I am a faithful friend.
I am good at listening,
And I'm loyal 'til the end.

Zephyr Dent (11)
Ysgol Cei Newydd, Cei Newydd

Who I Am

I am smart and funny
I really like bunnies
I am a nerd and I am cool
I really like school.

In the future I want to be a vet
I really like a pet
I can be mean
I really don't like beans.

I can be sad and happy
Also mad and snappy
I love the sea
I love me!

Chantelle Campbell (10)
Ysgol Cei Newydd, Cei Newydd

Me As A Tree

I am a tree,
My roots go far and wide,
I watch the birds sitting
In my branches,
As they roost,
I feel loved, and
I love them too,
I get bigger and bigger,
After time,
My leaves fall off,
Then I sprout new ones,
I love you,
And I hope,
You love me too.

Albert Brown (10)
Ysgol Cei Newydd, Cei Newydd

This Is Me

This is me,
Not quite five foot three,
Living by the sea,
In a town called New Quay.

This is me,
I like to drink tea,
I could drink,
One, two or three.

This is me,
Not quite five foot three,
Drinking tea by the sea,
My name is Tilly.

Tilly Taylor (11)
Ysgol Cei Newydd, Cei Newydd

Green

My favourite colour is green, just like green, thin, windy grass.
My favourite colour is green, just like as green as windy, green trees.
My favourite colour is green, just like a chameleon.
My favourite colour is green, a jumping frog.

Rhys Broom (9)
Ysgol Cei Newydd, Cei Newydd

All Me!

This poem is all about me,
Not anyone else, just me!
My heart is as light as a feather.
I really like the colour yellow.
I really like making loud echoes.
I mostly play with Lego.

Leon Zamorowski (10)
Ysgol Cei Newydd, Cei Newydd

Ingredients For Me

A pinch of kindness
A tablespoon of sweetness
A cup of smiles
A slice of intelligence
And bake for five minutes
Now you have me.

Tia Haslam (11)
Ysgol Cei Newydd, Cei Newydd

Aesthetic Me!

A dores wolves for life
M agnetic mind
B unks the bed all day
E legant fun
R ed and black is the best.

Amber Evans (9)
Ysgol Cei Newydd, Cei Newydd

Peaceful Puppy

Oh you peaceful puppy, you bring me so much joy!
I love you even more than my favourite toy.
You only ever see the good in me,
Being with you gives me wings and sets me free.
You're as beautiful as a rainbow and make me happy even in the rain.
With you by my side nothing seems a strain.
Your fur is so soft to touch
And that's another reason I love you so much.
You're as bright as a diamond and as cute as a bunny.
When you chase your tail it looks so funny!
Oh, peaceful puppy, you're as perfect as can be.
Oh, peaceful puppy, you help me to be me!

Lillian Facey (9)
Ysgol Garth Olwg, Church Village

The Playful Puppies

Playful puppies everywhere,
The owners let them go anywhere!
Climbing on the doors,
Jumping up the walls.
Ninety-nine times, but I don't know how!
They certainly make everyone happy now.
Your big, beautiful eyes shining in the light,
They are so bright like stars at night.
Your fur is as fluffy as a cloud,
But sometimes your barks are loud.
I still want to be like you,
But please, oh please don't chew my shoe!

Ella-Rose Alford
Ysgol Garth Olwg, Church Village

Wonderful Wide World!

Our world is full of happiness, but sometimes it can be sad.
Some people can be angry and some people can be bad.
We need to work together to make Earth a better place.
All this plastic all around us is a big disgrace.
If we all work together and put our rubbish in the bin
Our animals will stop vanishing.

This makes me so sad. This is me.

Layla Thomas (9)
Ysgol Garth Olwg, Church Village

I Wish, I Wish

Our animals are brave and fierce.
I wish, I wish I could be like you.
One day I will run as fast as a wolf and howl as loud as a siren.
I daydream about our animals when I'm brushing my sharp, fang-like teeth.
I wish, I wish, I wish.

Gruffudd Evans (9)
Ysgol Garth Olwg, Church Village

YOUNG WRITERS INFORMATION

We hope you have enjoyed reading this book – and that you will continue to in the coming years.

If you're the parent or family member of an enthusiastic poet or story writer, do visit our website **www.youngwriters.co.uk/subscribe** and sign up to receive news, competitions, writing challenges and tips, activities and much, much more! There's lots to keep budding writers motivated!

If you would like to order further copies of this book, or any of our other titles, then please give us a call or order via your online account.

Young Writers
Remus House
Coltsfoot Drive
Peterborough
PE2 9BF
(01733) 890066
info@youngwriters.co.uk

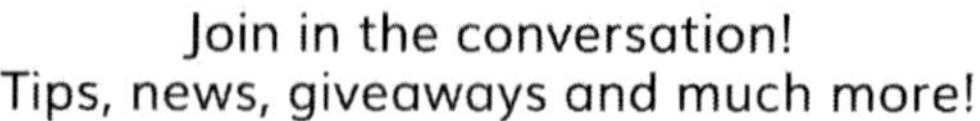